I WILL NOT

StarWalk
Kids
Media

For my beloved father, "Zimo,"
who continues to be my inspiration,
and for the children of Palestine and Israel.

—N.F.

For those who would not lose hope.

—O.E.

I WILL NOT

by **Naila Farouky**

illustrated **by Ora Eitan**

I will not call for death.

I will not speak the words

that call for the death of the "other."

I will not seek to avenge through death,

the sister, the mother,

the father or brother.

I will not cry, "If you kill us,

then we are right to kill!"

and then question, in anguish,

"Where has our humanity gone?"

I will not call for death.

You ask me to justify

how I can stand for my enemy;

I reply only, "I know no enemy."

I know war and pain

Fear and injustice;

I know blood and tears

Corruption and failed armistice.

I see bodies, bloodied and strewn about.

I see them—I hear you and I feel the pain—

I see mothers wailing for the loss of their children.

I see children grasping the air seeking the comforting

arms of their slain mothers.

I see fathers burying their babes in white cloths.

I see children with despair in their eyes

at sights they will never forget.

I hear of sirens unheeded

For to heed them means you have

some place to hide.

I hear tales of the warnings

that come in the night.

The warnings that parents

must choose to ignore

for to obey them must mean

you have somewhere to go.

I will not call for death.

"But they want you to die,

they demand it, can't you see?"

"You're a traitor, a coward, how can this be?"

I see it—I know—do you think me so blind?

I hear it, I fear it, but I know where I stand.

As the world sits in wait, to watch and to plead

Those I cherish and love have no choice but to bleed.

Our humanity challenged, I offer you this:

We must search inside, for it lives within us.

It is not to be found in

the barrel of a gun

Or a bomb, or a funeral,

a surah or a psalm.

It is in your heart and your

head and your womb

In your words and your dreams

and the threads of your loom,

In your hopes for your children

that they shall not hate.

For their hopes and their dreams

are their future and fate!

So abandon the sirens, the bombs and your might;

Hold your hands to the heavens and scream in the night.

Beg for mercy, for respite, for heart and for will

But do not seize the urge to go for the kill.

And repeat to yourself,

for as long as it takes,

I will not call for death

no matter how much it aches.

I will not.

THE STORY BEHIND THIS BOOK

The Gaza Strip, where many Palestinian people live, is sandwiched between Israel, Egypt and the Mediterranean Sea. This narrow strip of land has been a hotspot in the Israel-Palestinian conflict for many years.

In July of 2014, the world watched with great sadness as violence erupted once again between Israelis and Palestinians in the Gaza Strip. The fighting continued for 50 days. Night after night, rocket fire from Gaza and air strikes from Israel rocked the homes of innocent citizens in both territories. A Palestinian-Egyptian writer and former Sesame Street producer named Naila Farouky was particularly saddened by these events because she knew and worked with people in both territories. Wide awake in the middle of the night, she wrote this poem to express the shock and despair she felt at what she was hearing from friends, Israeli, Palestinian and others. "Friends of mine on both sides were grieving, saying things like 'How can they be killing our children?' And then in the next sentence saying: 'May God one day show you the same torture and kill your children before your eyes.' When good people are talking like this," says Naila, "we will never get anywhere. The biggest challenge in maintaining your humanity is when your values are tested by events like these."

Our team at StarWalk Kids Media quickly determined that we wanted to make Naila's poem into a book . . . a book that we would publish not only in English, but also in Arabic and Hebrew, the languages spoken by Palestinians and Israelis. We approached an Israeli illustrator named Ora Eitan, whose powerful style and rich use of color would give visual power to the stark, emphatic poem. Ora responded deeply to the poem and was eager to take on the challenge. Naila agreed. "I loved the idea that not only is Ora a great artist, she's Israeli. We were really walking the walk and talking the talk."

We hope that our readers will be inspired by this small-but-mighty vow, shared by a Palestinian writer and an Israeli artist in the face of violence: I WILL NOT.

On the pages that follow are translations of this poem, first in Arabic, then in Hebrew.

ابدأ ...

لن أطَالِبَ بالمَوتِ ولن اطْلُبَ حضورَه

تُحَاوِلَ أن تَقْنِعَني فَتُعْلِمُني، يتمنون الموتَ لك ويطلبونه

تَتَهمَني بالخيانةِ والجبنِ، تُحَاكِمَني فتقول هراء ما اقوله

لكن اسمعني، انا رأيتُ و عرفتُ، صدقني ليس العَمَى نصيبي

بَلَى، سَمِعْتُ وخِفْتُ وهَبِتُ ولكني لست حائرٌ

اعرفُ موطئَ اقْدامي ومَوقِفي ومَقَامي وانا على نفسي رقيبي

واعلم أنَّه وقتَما يقفُ العالمُ مشاهداً مترافعاً ينعمُ بنعمةِ الانتظارِ

ينزفُ دمَ احبائي وأعزاءي دون اختيار

لهذا، وقبل أن تقل لي أنَّ انسانيةَ الانسانَ قد ماتت

اقدمت على الانْتِحَارِ، أقدم انا لك الدعوةَ

لنبحث سوياً في داخلِنا، جدياً

فالإنسانية حيةٌ تُرْزَق في الاعماقِ

لن تجدها في فوهةِ البندقيةِ

في قنبلةٍ، في جنازةٍ، في سورةٍ قرآنيةٍ أو مزمورٍ

بل هي في قلبِك وفكرِك

الانسانيةُ في رحم الانسانِ

في كلماتِك وأحلامك وفي الخيوطِ التي تغزلُها على النولِ

في آمِلِك أن يكبرَ صغارك بدون كراهيةٍ ولا جور

واعلم أن غدَ الصغارُ ومصيرهم مرهون بآمالِهم وأحلامِهم

ليس بِنَحر الصدورِ

فاترك الصفافيرَ والنذيرَ، وانسى القنابلَ وبأسك الغفيرَ

ارفع يديك للسماءِ واصرخ، اطلب الرحمةَ، اطلب مهلةً

اطلب شجاعةَ القلبَ ونفاذَ العزمَ

وامتنع عن الركض وراء كل رغبةٍ في القتلِ

ردد لنفسك مراراً وتكراراً

لن أطَالِبَ بالمَوتِ ولن اطْلُبَ حضورَه

ابَدأ ...

مهما ازداد ألمي وكربي

لن أطَالِبَ بالمَوتِ، لن أفعَلَ ذلك...

لــن ...

لن أطَالبَ بالمَوتِ ولن اطْلبَ حضورَه

ابَداً ...

لن أطَالبَ بالمَوتِ لهم، لن الْفظَ الحُكمَ الأخيرَ

هل بالمَوتِ يُشْفى غَليلي؟ وبالقَتْلِ يكون انْتقامي؟

من أخٍ وأختٍ؟ من أبٍ وأمٍ؟

لن أهْتفَ: قتلكم محلل فأنتم قد قتلتمونا

ثم اعود مُتسائلاً، هل هذا هو الانسان؟ هل هكذا الدمُ يهونَ؟

ابَداً ...

لن أطَالبَ بالمَوتِ ولن اطْلبَ حضورَه

تسألني، لما ادافع عن عدوي

اسمعني، انا لا اعرف لي عَدَواً

عَرَفْت الحَرْبَ والألمَ، رافقت الخوفَ والظلمَ

اسمعني، فأنا عَرَفْت الدمَ والدمعَ

ألفْت الفَسادَ والفَشَلَ

فشل السُلم والهُدنة

لا تساءلني، وصدقني

رأيت البشرَ جثثاً متفشية تغلفها الدماء

صدقني رأيتهم ، انا مثلك يهزني الحزنُ والألمُ

رأيت وسَمِعتَ عويلَ الأمِ، وكل أم فقدت صغارها دون انقضاءِ

رأيت لهفةَ الرضيعَ وكل رضيع يبحث في الهواءِ

عن يدَ أمَه الفقيدة لتضمه بلا رجاءِ

رأيت الأب ، وكل أب يُنَزِلَ رضيعه في التراب

بعد أن واراه وجَفف دَمَه في أوشحةٍ بيضاءِ

رأيت طفلاً وكل طفل تقهقرت عيناه وراء سدَ من اليأسِ إبان مشهدَ مريع لن ينساه

سمعت نذيرَ صافراتٍ دوت ولم يعرها احد انتباه

فما فائدة النذير وليس هناك مكان للاختباء

سمعت حكاياتٍ عن وعيدٍ وإشعاراتٍ تَدُقُ ابوابَ البيوتَ ليلا فيصرفها الآباء

حقا هل لهم من خيارٍ وخارج الابواب ما لهم من ايواءِ؟

"אבל הם רוצים שתמותי, הם לא יוותרו,
עינייך עצומות?"
"פחדנית את, בוגדת, איך זה יכול להיות?"
הכל אני יודעת-רואה—זה מטיל עלי מורא,
הכל אני שומעת, אבל עמדתי ברורה.
ממתין, מביט, מפציר כל העולם,
ואהובי ויקירי מדממים בעל כורחם.
האנושיות שלנו נתונה בסכנה, ואני מזמינה:
חפשו אותה בקרבכם, זה מקום משכנה.

לא נמצא אותה בקניהם של רובים
בפצצות ולוויות, בסורות ומזמורי תהילים.
היא ברחם, בראש, בלב המקווה
במילים, בחלומות, ובנול הטווה.

בַּשאיפות למען ילדיכם, שלא תפַעם שנאה בלבם
כי תקוותיהם וחלומותיהם הם עתידם וגורלם!

הרפו אפוא מאזעקות, פצצות, יד חזקה;
הושיטו זרועות אל שמי הלילה והשמיעו זעקה.

התחננו לרחמים, להפוגה, ללב ולרצון
אך אל תחושו אל ההרג בלהט חיפזון.

וחִזרו ואמרו, כל כמה שנדרש,
לא אקרא למוות, גם לא מתוך כאב נורא,
למוות לא אקרא.

לא אקרא לְמוות

מאת נאילה פארוקי   איורים: אורה איתן

לא אקרא לְמוות.

לא אוֹמַר מילים אשר קוראות לְמוֹת ה"אחרים".
לא אבקש לְאם, אב, אח, אחות, נקמת דמים.
לא אקרא, "אם תהרגו בנו זכותנו להרוג!"
ולא אשאל אחר כך במצוקה,
"היכן היא האנושיות?"
לא אקרא לְמוות.

תובעים ממני הצדקות:
'כיצד זה תעמדי לצד אויב?'
כל שאומַר הוא: 'אינני מכירה אויב.'
אני מכירה מלחמה וכאב
פחד ועוולות;
מכירה דם ודמעות
שחיתות ושביתות נשק כושלות.

אני רואה גוויות, מכוסות דם, מוטלות,
אני רואה אותן – שומעת אֶתכם וחשה בַּכאב –

אני רואה אימהות מקוננות על אובדן ילדיהן.
אני רואה ילדים מגששים באוויר אחרי חיבוקן המנחם של אמהות שחוטות
אני רואה אבות קוברים עוללים בבגדים לבנים.

אני רואה ילדים ובעיניהם ייאוש ממראות שלעולם לא ישכחו.

אני שומעת על אזעקות שלא שעו להן
אפשר לשעות להן אם יש מקום מחבוא.
אני שומעת סיפורים על אזהרות בלילה
על הורים שנאלצו לבחור להתעלם
לציית פירושו שיש לאן ללכת.
לא אקרא לְמוות.

ABOUT THE AUTHOR
AND ILLUSTRATOR

Naila Farouky is a Peabody Award-winning Executive Producer with extensive experience in developing and producing quality children's programming. Of Palestinian-Egyptian origin, with dual Jordanian and American citizenship, Naila has worked as an Executive Producer and Project Manager on *Sesame Street* co-productions in 17 countries around the world, including Jordan, Palestine, Egypt and across Sub-Saharan Africa. She is currently the CEO of the Arab Foundations Forum based in Amman, Jordan.

Ora Eitan was born Ora Sandhhus in Tel Aviv and graduated from the Bzalel Academy of Art and Design in Jerusalem, where she later taught illustration for many years. Ora has illustrated more than 100 books for children and is the recipient of numerous distinguished awards and honors, including a nomination for the Hans Christian Andersen Award and two Hans Christian Andersen Certificates of Honor. Her work has been exhibited at museums and galleries throughout Israel and abroad, and some of her books have been translated into Arabic. Today, Ora paints, illustrates, and spends time with her five grandchildren, Tomer, Amit, Erez, Alon and Rona.

Arabic Translation by Tagreid Abu Hassabo

Hebrew Translation by Lee Evron-Vaknin

Text copyright © 2015 by Naila Farouky
Illustrations copyright © 2015 by Ora Eita
All rights reserved.
Published by StarWalk Kids Media

www.StarWalkKids.com

ISBN 978-1-63083-540-8

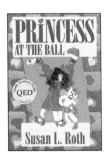
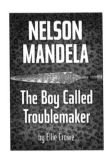

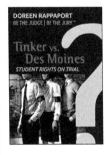
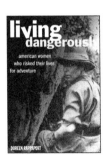
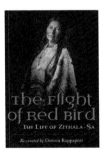

This is the true, inspiring story of Malala Yousafzai, a young Pakistani girl who stands up and speaks out for every child's right to education. Though she and two of her schoolmates were targeted by a Taliban gunman, a life-threatening injury only strengthened her resolve. Malala spoke at the U.N. on her 16th birthday in 2012, nine months after she was shot.

Malala is a miracle in pink. She is a warrior with words. And she wants every boy and girl to stand up and speak out for the millions of children who are not able to go to school all over the world.

Author and journalist Karen Leggett Abouraya, past President of the Children's Book Guild in Washington, D.C. and author of *Hands Around the Library: Protecting Egypt's Treasured Books*, brings Malala's story to life for young readers. Malala's story is more than a biography of a brave and outspoken girl. It is a testament to the power of education to change the world for boys and girls everywhere.

"A MOVING REAL-LIFE STORY, WELL-TOLD AND BEAUTIFULLY ILLUSTRATED— A nonfiction picture book about a young Pakistani activist who believes that education is a basic human right. [Author Karen Leggett Abouraya's] words and her storytelling are clear and moving . . . [L.C. Wheatley's] illustrations meet the high standards set by the text, using cut paper and occasional photographs to create skillful compositions." — *KIRKUS REVIEWS*

Available Now in Print & Digital

CPSIA information can be obtained at www.ICGtesting.com
Printed in the USA
BVOW11s0937190815

414005BV00017B/63/P